We Want a Dog!

Written by Abie Longstaff

Illustrated by Mar Ferrero

OXFORD
UNIVERSITY PRESS

OXFORD
UNIVERSITY PRESS

Great Clarendon Street, Oxford, OX2 6DP, United Kingdom

Oxford University Press is a department of the University
of Oxford. It furthers the University's objective of excellence
in research, scholarship, and education by publishing
worldwide. Oxford is a registered trade mark of Oxford
University Press in the UK and in certain other countries

Text © Abie Longstaff 2017
Illustrations © Mar Ferrero 2017
Inside cover notes written by Karra McFarlane

The moral rights of the author have been asserted

First published 2017

British Library Cataloguing in Publication Data
Data available

ISBN: 978-0-19-841500-8

10 9 8 7 6 5 4 3 2 1

Paper used in the production of this book is a natural, recyclable product
made from wood grown in sustainable forests. The manufacturing process
conforms to the environmental regulations of the country of origin.

Printed in China by Golden Cup

Acknowledgements

Series Editor: Nikki Gamble

Anna and Max went to the park.

They spotted an animal in the trees.

4

5

Anna and Max took Spot home.

7

Spot got into the bath.

Then Spot got into bed.
He looked at a book.

Max looked at Spot's dark spots.

Anna looked at Spot's long neck.

Spot is not a dog!

9

Anna and Max took Spot back
to the park.

Spot ran home to his mum.

Max was sad.
Anna was sad, too.

But then ...

Look!

Spot was back! Anna and
Max patted him.

Then Max spotted an animal
in the trees.

15

16